It's another great book from CGP...

If you're studying KS3 Maths (ages 11-14), this book is a brilliant
way to prepare for any assessments your school might set you.

It's packed with test-style questions, all set at foundation level — that's
what would have been called Levels 3-6 in the old (pre-2014) Curriculum.

We've even included a **free** Online Edition you can read on your computer or tablet!

How to get your free Online Edition

Just go to **cgpbooks.co.uk/extras** and enter this code...

0057 5491 3963 0784

By the way, this code only works for one person. If somebody else has used
this book before you, they might have already claimed the Online Edition.

CGP — still the best! ☺

Our sole aim here at CGP is to produce the highest quality books —
carefully written, immaculately presented and dangerously close to being funny.

Then we work our socks off to get them out to you
— at the cheapest possible prices.

Contents

☑ Use the tick boxes to check off the topics you've completed.

Section 4 — Geometry and Measures

Section 5 — Probability and Statistics

Published by CGP

Editors: Rob Harrison, Shaun Harrogate, Ruth Wilbourne
Contributors: Andy Ballard, Pamela Chatley, Jane Chow, Mark Moody, Jeanette Whiteman
With thanks to Janet Dickinson and Simon Little for the proofreading.

ISBN: 978 1 78294 172 9

www.cgpbooks.co.uk
Printed by Elanders Ltd, Newcastle upon Tyne.
Clipart from Corel®
Based on the classic CGP style created by Richard Parsons.

How to Use This Book

The smileys show you how difficult the questions are.

These ones test your basic skills.

These questions are a bit more challenging.

These ones are pretty tough.

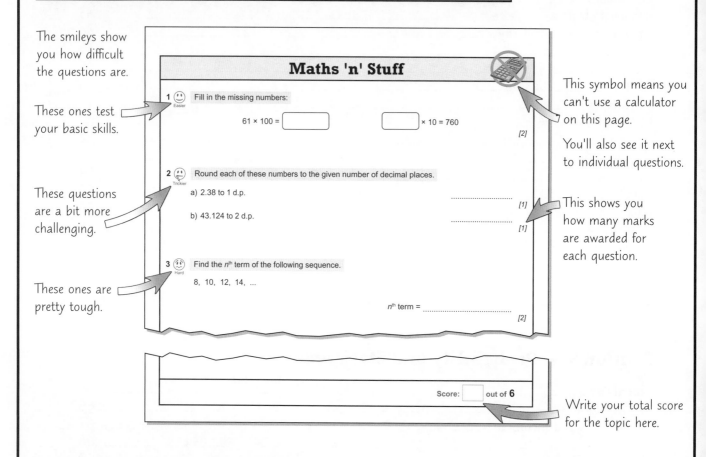

Maths 'n' Stuff

1 Easier — Fill in the missing numbers:

$61 \times 100 =$ [ ]   [ ] $\times 10 = 760$

[2]

2 Trickier — Round each of these numbers to the given number of decimal places.

a) 2.38 to 1 d.p.

.... [1]

b) 43.124 to 2 d.p.

.... [1]

3 Hard — Find the nth term of the following sequence.

8, 10, 12, 14, ...

n^{th} term = ...

[2]

Score: [ ] out of **6**

This symbol means you can't use a calculator on this page.

You'll also see it next to individual questions.

This shows you how many marks are awarded for each question.

Write your total score for the topic here.

Follow these Top Test Tips...

1) Always, always, always make sure you <u>read the question properly</u>.
   For example, if the question asks you to give your answer in metres, <u>don't</u> give it in centimetres.

2) <u>Underline</u> the information that you <u>need</u> to <u>answer the question</u>
   There can be a lot of waffle in test questions — this'll help you pick out the important bits.

3) Show <u>each step</u> in your <u>working</u>.
   You're less likely to make a mistake if you write things out in stages. And even if your final answer's wrong, you'll probably pick up <u>some marks</u> if your teacher can see that your <u>method</u> is right.

4) Check that your answer is <u>sensible</u>.
   Worked out an angle of 450° or 0.045° in a triangle? You've probably gone wrong somewhere...

5) Make sure you give your answer to the right <u>degree of accuracy</u>.
   The question might ask you to round to a certain number of <u>significant figures</u> or <u>decimal places</u>.
   So make sure you do just that, otherwise you'll almost certainly lose marks.

6) Write your answers as <u>clearly</u> as you can.
   If your teacher can't read your answer you won't get any marks, even if it's right.

These rules won't help if you haven't learnt the stuff in the first place. So make sure you do as much practice as you can.

Ordering Numbers and Place Value

1 😀 Easier   Peter has been looking at some facts about the town he lives in.

    a) There are three hundred and nineteen teachers living in the town.
Write this number in figures.

                                                                    .... [1]

    b) The total number of people living in the town is 20 605. Write the number 20 605 in words.

    ....

    .... [1]

    c) 15 843 adults live in the town.
In the number 15 843, the figure 4 has the value of 40. What is the value of the figure 5?

                                                                 .... [1]

2 😀 Easier   Nick has six number cards.

$$\boxed{1} \quad \boxed{8} \quad \boxed{7} \quad \boxed{3} \quad \boxed{6} \quad \boxed{2}$$

    Nick is asked to arrange the cards to make different numbers.

    a) Write down the largest number Nick can make.

                                                       .... [1]

    b) What is the smallest five-digit number Nick can make?

                                                   .... [1]

    c) What is the closest number to 260 that Nick can make?

                                                   .... [1]

    d) Write down in words the smallest four-digit number Nick can make.

    ....

    .... [1]

Ordering Numbers and Place Value

3 😀
Easier

Put each set of numbers in order of size, starting with the smallest.

a) 68   7432   985   7480   73   967

....

[1]

b) 4.8   5.72   3.09   4.79   5.17   3.5

....

[1]

4 😀
Easier

The table shows the heights and weights of five children.

Name of child	Height (metres)	Weight (kilograms)
Emily	0.88	18.06
Georgina	0.858	18.5
Thomas	0.904	20.3
Imogen	0.942	20.09
Elliot	0.82	18.1

a) Write down the names of the children in height order starting with the shortest child.

....

[1]

b) Write down the names of the children in weight order starting with the heaviest child.

....

[1]

5 😐
Trickier

Graham recorded the weight, in grams, of five insects and got these results.

0.054   0.578   0.049   0.0064   0.044

Put the weights in order starting with the lightest weight.

....

[1]

Score: ☐ out of **12**

Add, Subtract, Multiply and Divide

1 😀
Easier

Chris and Sabrina are thinking of ways of getting from one number to another.

a) Chris thinks of three different ways of getting from 5 to 20.
Fill in the boxes with +, −, × or ÷ to make each of Chris's calculations correct.

5 ☐ 15 = 20

5 ☐ 4 = 20

5 ☐ 2 ☐ 10 = 20

[3]

b) Sabrina finds a method, using one operation, that changes 20 to 5.
Her method also changes 32 to 8. What is Sabrina's method?

....

[1]

2 😀
Easier

Fill in the missing numbers below so that the calculations are correct.

a) 94 + 28 = 90 + ☐

[1]

b) 24 × 4 = 12 × ☐

[1]

3 😀
Trickier

Look at these calculations.

Remember to use BODMAS.

Tick (✓) ones that are correct. Cross (✗) ones that are wrong.

Calculation	✓ or ✗
(10 + 2) − 4 = 10 + 2 − 4	
10 + (2 × 4) = 10 + 2 × 4	
10 × (4 + 2) = 10 × 4 + 2	
(10 − 4) ÷ 2 = 10 − 4 ÷ 2	
(10 ÷ 2) × 4 − 2 = 10 ÷ 2 × 4 − 2	

[2]

Score: ☐ out of **8**

Addition and Subtraction

1
Easier

Write the answers to these calculations in the boxes provided.

```
    4 2 6
  +   8 7
  ☐☐☐
```

```
    7 8 2
  - 1 7 3
  ☐☐☐
```

[2]

2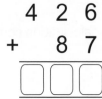
Easier

Alex and Duncan are stamp collectors. Alex has 1023 stamps and Duncan has 632 stamps. How many more stamps does Alex have than Duncan?

.... [1]

3
Trickier

ABC Theatre Group is putting on a production of "Sleeping Beauty".
The ticket prices for members, non-members and children are shown below.

> Ticket Prices
>
> Members.................... £5.75
> Non-members.............£9.50
> Children (under 16).... £6.25

a) Amanda and Julie are both over 16. Amanda is a member of the theatre but Julie isn't.
What will be the total cost for Amanda and Julie to go and see the production?

£ ....
[1]

b) Amanda's 8 year old sister also wants to see the show with them.
How much change will they get from £30 if they pay for all three tickets together?

£ ....
[2]

Score: ☐ out of **6**

Multiplying by 10, 100, etc.

1 😀 Easier Fill in the missing numbers:

$61 × 100 =$ [＿＿＿＿＿]   [＿＿＿＿＿] $× 10 = 760$

[2]

2 😀 Easier The numbers below were the winning raffle tickets in the SaveTheSloths raffle.

[480] [25] [3200] [2005] [48] [302] [32] [205]

a) Pick two tickets so that the number on one ticket is 10 times bigger than the other.

.... and ....

[1]

b) Pick two tickets so that the number on one ticket is 100 times bigger than the other.

.... and ....

[1]

3 😀 Easier Three numbers, *a*, *b* and *c*, are worked out as follows:

$a = 0.602 × 1000$ $b = 6.2 × 10$ $c = 0.065 × 10\,000$

Which is the largest number, *a*, *b* or *c*? Show your working.

....

[2]

4 🙂 Trickier A small packet of crisps costs 22p and a large packet of crisps costs 42p.

Bob buys 50 small packets of crisps. Matt buys 30 large packets of crisps.
How much more does Matt spend than Bob?

£ ....

[3]

Score: [＿＿＿] out of **9**

Section 1 — Numbers

Dividing by 10, 100, etc.

1 😃 Fill in the missing numbers:
Easier

a) 500 ÷ 10 = [   ]

[1]

b) 3400 ÷ [   ] = 34

[1]

c) [   ] ÷ 1000 = 820

[1]

2 😃 18 700 people attended a football match.
Easier

a) 1 in every 10 people bought a match programme. How many programmes were sold?

....

[1]

b) 1 in every 100 people bought a hamburger. How many hamburgers were sold?

....

[1]

3 😃 A school bought 60 Maths books at a total cost of £1200.
Trickier

a) How much does one book cost?

£ ....

[1]

A book is made up of a front and back cover and 300 pages.
The front and back covers are 1 mm thick each.
The total thickness of the book is 38 mm.

b) Work out the thickness of one page of the book.

.... mm

[2]

Score: [   ] out of **8**

Multiplying Without a Calculator

1 🙂 Easier There are 17 onions in each jar of pickled onions. How many onions are in 39 jars?

.... [1]

2 🙂 Easier A doughnut costs 36p. A cream cake costs 65p.

a) Find the cost, in pounds, of 8 doughnuts.

£ .... [1]

b) Find the cost, in pounds, of 18 cream cakes.

£ .... [1]

c) Jenny buys 8 doughnuts and 18 cream cakes.
How much change does she receive from £20? Show your working.

£ .... [2]

3 🙂 Trickier A train ticket from Manchester to London costs £67.
A flight from Manchester to London costs £113.

How much more would it cost in total for 13 people to get a flight from
Manchester to London rather than getting the train?

£ .... [3]

Score: ⬚ out of **8**

Dividing Without a Calculator

1 😊 A box can hold a maximum of 6 eggs.
Easier

a) How many boxes are needed for 336 eggs?

....
[1]

b) How many boxes are needed for 608 eggs?

....
[2]

c) 55 chickens lay 9 eggs each. How many boxes are needed to pack these eggs?

....
[3]

2 😊 The table shows the amount of money three boys save each week.
Easier

	Money saved per week
Andy	£5
Lewis	£8
Rick	£4

a) How many weeks does Lewis have to save for in order to buy a £128 MP3 player?

....
[1]

b) Andy wants to buy a games console for £263.
How many weeks does he have to save for before he can buy it?

....
[2]

c) Rick wants to buy a £100 mobile phone. He has already saved up £40.
How many more weeks does he have to save for?

....
[2]

Score: [   ] out of **11**

Negative Numbers

1
Easier

Put the following numbers in order of size, smallest first.

-12   -1   -5   7   0   -4   -6

.... [1]

2
Easier

The Christmas Day temperatures in certain cities were recorded and listed in the table below.

City	Temp °C
Amsterdam	-1
Madrid	6
Montreal	-7
New York	-3
Paris	4
Venice	2

a) Which city was the coldest?   ....

[1]

b) What was the difference in the temperature between Paris and Montreal?

................°C

[1]

c) The next day the temperature in New York fell by 12°C. What was the new temperature?

................°C

[1]

d) How many of the cities were colder than Venice but warmer than Montreal?

....

[1]

3
Trickier

Fill in the missing numbers below so that the calculations are correct.

a) -8 × 8 = ☐

Double check you've used the correct signs.

[1]

b) -42 ÷ -7 = ☐

[1]

c) -9 × ☐ = 72

[1]

Score: ☐ out of **8**

Special Types of Number

1 Easier   Gemma has six coins in her purse:

1p   2p   5p   10p   20p   50p

     a) She buys sweets using all her even valued coins. She does not get any change. How much do the sweets cost?

                                                .... *[1]*

     b) How much money does she have left in her purse?

                                                .... *[1]*

2 Easier   Look at this list of numbers:

| 1 | 4 | 8 | 16 | 25 | 27 | 38 | 49 | 55 | 64 |

     a) Write down all the even numbers.   *[1]*

     b) Write down all the odd square numbers.   *[1]*

     c) Write down all the odd cube numbers.   *[1]*

     d) Which numbers are both square and cube numbers?   *[1]*

3 Hard   Find the value of:

     a) $9^2 - 3^2$

                                                 .... *[2]*

     b) $10^3 + 10^2 + 10$

                                                 .... *[2]*

     c) $5^3 - 6^2$

                                                 .... *[2]*

Score: [ ] out of **12**

Prime Numbers

1 :) Easier   Write down:

    a) an even prime number.   ....

                                                       [1]

    b) the first six prime numbers.

                                                       [1]

    c) all the prime numbers between 25 and 35.

                                                       [2]

2 :) Trickier   Show that:

    a) 89 is a prime number.

                                                       [1]

    b) 91 is not a prime number.

                                                       [1]

3 :) Trickier   Here are four number cards.

         4   **7**   **2**   **3**

    a) Choose two of the number cards to make a prime number less than 35.

                                                  .... *[1]*

    b) Using two of the number cards, write down a prime number greater than 50.
       Show that the number you have written is prime.

                                                       [2]

Score: [   ] out of **9**

Multiples and Factors

1 😊 Easier

1	2	3	4	5	6	7	8	9	10
11	12	13	14	15	16	17	18	19	20
21	22	23	24	25	26	27	28	29	30
31	32	33	34	35	36	37	38	39	40

In the number grid opposite:

a) Circle all of the multiples of 3.

[1]

b) Put a cross through all the multiples of 7.

[1]

2 😊 Easier — List all of the factors of the following:

a) 12

....

[1]

b) 40

....

[1]

c) 12 **and** 40

....

[1]

3 😛 Trickier — Here is a set of winning Lotto numbers.

(30) (1) (24) (8) (48) (27)

a) Which Lotto numbers are multiples of both 4 and 6?

....

[1]

b) Which Lotto number is a multiple of 3 and a factor of 54?

....

[1]

4 😟 Hard — Factor trees allow you to find the prime factors of a number.

a) Complete the factor tree.

84

6   14

◯   ◯   ◯   ◯

[2]

b) Express 84 as a product of prime factors.

....

[1]

Multiply the numbers in your answer together to check they give 84.

Score: ☐ out of **10**

LCM and HCF

1 Trickier — Find the lowest common multiple of 4 and 5.

.... [1]

2 Trickier — What is the highest common factor of 42 and 24?

.... [1]

3 Hard — What is the highest common factor of 10, 18 **and** 22?

Find the largest number that's a factor of all 3 numbers.

.... [2]

4 Hard — There are two drummers in a brass band. One hits his drum every 8 beats and the other hits his drum every 10 beats. They have just played at the same time.

How many beats will it be before they play at the same time again?

Write out the beats each drummer plays on.

.... beats

[2]

Score: [ ] out of **6**

Section 1 — Numbers

Fractions, Decimals & Percentages

1
Trickier

Convert each of the following:

a) 0.83 into a fraction

.... [1]

b) 8% into a decimal

.... [1]

c) $\frac{3}{5}$ into a percentage

.... [1]

2
Trickier

Fill in the missing values in the table.

Fraction	Decimal	Percentage
$\frac{3}{4}$		
	0.8	
		51%

[3]

3
Trickier

Hassan carried out a survey of cars passing the school gates.

a) 43% of the cars were red. What is this as a fraction?

.... [1]

b) 3% were sports cars. Write this as a decimal.

.... [1]

4
Hard

Which of these is greater:

a) 0.42 or $\frac{2}{5}$? Show your working.

.... [2]

b) 12% or $\frac{3}{20}$? Show your working.

.... [2]

Score: [ ] out of **12**

Section 1 — Numbers

Fractions

1 Cancel these fractions to their simplest form.
Easier

   a) $\dfrac{12}{20}$

....

[1]

   b) $\dfrac{44}{100}$

....

[1]

2 Trickier Five numbered cards are shown below.

   Choose 3 cards to complete the two equivalent fractions below.

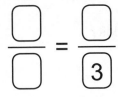

[1]

3 Trickier Georgina and Amie both measure the length of one of their little toes, in inches. Their results are shown below.

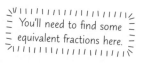

You'll need to find some equivalent fractions here.

| Georgina: $\dfrac{5}{8}$ inches | Amie: $\dfrac{7}{12}$ inches |

   Which of the girls has the longer little toe? Show your working.

....

[2]

4 Trickier Convert each of these:

   a) $4\dfrac{1}{5}$ into an improper fraction.

....

[1]

   b) $\dfrac{22}{9}$ into a mixed number.

....

[1]

Fractions

5
Trickier

Find the following:

a) $\frac{2}{5}$ of 195 kg

.... kg
[1]

b) $\frac{3}{7}$ of 231 miles

.... miles
[1]

6
Trickier

Jane has £55 in her purse.
She spends $\frac{4}{11}$ of this on a bag and $\frac{3}{5}$ on a computer game.

a) How much did the bag cost?

£ ....
[1]

b) How much money does she have left?

£ ....
[2]

7 Hard

Work out the following. Give your answers as fractions in their simplest form.

a) $\frac{4}{9} + \frac{1}{6}$

....
[2]

b) $\frac{4}{5} - \frac{3}{4}$

....
[2]

8 Hard

Work out the following. Give your answers as fractions in their simplest form.

a) $\frac{5}{7} \times \frac{3}{5}$

....
[1]

b) $\frac{5}{11} \div \frac{2}{3}$

....
[1]

Score: ☐ out of **18**

Percentages

1 😀 Easier   Find 15% of 180.

Try finding 10% first, then halve that to find 5%. Add them together to get 15%.

.... [1]

2 🙂 Trickier   Mark, a builder, charges £1500 plus VAT to build an extension. The VAT is charged at 20%. Work out how much VAT he charges.

£ .... [1]

3 😐 Trickier   Sinead buys an old vase from a car boot sale for £88. She sells the vase for 66% of the price she paid. How much did she sell the vase for?

£ .... [1]

4 🙁 Trickier   Lucy receives £75 as a birthday present.

a) She spends £24 on a watch. What is this as a percentage of £75?

.... % [1]

b) She saves the rest of the money. What percentage of the money does she save?

.... % [1]

5 😟 Hard   Ruth's Rags has just increased all of its prices. Last week, a shirt at Ruth's Rags cost £40. This week the price of the same shirt is £64.

Find the new price as a percentage of the old price.

.... % [1]

Score: ☐ out of **6**

Rounding Numbers

1 Easier Complete the table by rounding each number to the nearest 10, 100 and 1000.

	nearest 10	nearest 100	nearest 1000
654			
5349			

[2]

2 Trickier Round each of these numbers to the given number of decimal places.

a) 2.38 to 1 d.p.

....
[1]

b) 43.124 to 2 d.p.

....
[1]

3 Hard Round each of these numbers to the given number of significant figures.

a) 3545 to 2 s.f.

....
[1]

b) 96.45 to 3 s.f.

....
[1]

4 Hard Fewcastle United's highest ever league attendance is 68 386. Round this number:

a) to the nearest thousand.

....
[1]

b) to the nearest ten.

....
[1]

c) to 3 significant figures.

....
[1]

5 Hard A newspaper reports that the population of Sheffield is 550 000 people.

If this figure is correct to 2 significant figures, circle the
numbers below which the exact population could be.

552 054   502 202   544 599   549 152   555 478

[1]

Score: ☐ out of **10**

Accuracy and Estimating

1 😟 Hard — Calculate the rounding error when 87 is given correct to 1 significant figure.

.... [1]

2 😟 Hard — Calculate the rounding error when 54.846 is given correct to 2 decimal places.

.... [1]

3 😟 Hard — Estimate the answers to the following calculations.

a) 51.2×11

.... [1]

b) $62.9 \div 29$

.... [1]

c) $\dfrac{301}{9.9 \times 2.9}$

.... [2]

4 😟 Hard — A single mattress is 94.8 cm wide and 196.4 cm long.

a) Find an estimate for the area of the mattress by rounding each number to 1 s.f.

.... cm^2 [2]

b) What does your estimate become if you round each number to 2 s.f. instead?

.... cm^2 [2]

Score: ☐ out of **10**

Powers

1 Evaluate $1.2^3 - 0.4^2$.

....
[1]

2 What is $3^4 - 2^5$?

....
[2]

3 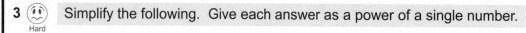 Simplify the following. Give each answer as a power of a single number.

a) $3^4 \times 3^5$

....
[1]

b) $5^{11} \div 5^3$

....
[1]

4 Given that $2^{12} = 4096$, what is 2^{11} equal to?

....
[2]

5 Evaluate the following:

Use the power rules to help you.
Start by simplifying the numerator.

a) $\dfrac{2^9 \times 1^{22}}{2^7}$

....
[2]

b) $\dfrac{5^{10} \div 5^8}{5^0}$

....
[2]

Score: ☐ out of **11**

Square Roots and Cube Roots

1 Trickier Find both square roots of these numbers.

a) 16

.... [2]

b) 81

.... [2]

2 Trickier Evaluate the following:

a) $\sqrt[3]{1728}$

.... [1]

b) $\sqrt[4]{256}$

.... [1]

3 Hard Some square numbers are given in the box below.

$17^2 = 289 \qquad 18^2 = 324 \qquad 19^2 = 361 \qquad 20^2 = 400 \qquad 21^2 = 441 \qquad 22^2 = 484$

Use this information to evaluate the following:

a) $\sqrt{324} + \sqrt{441}$

.... [2]

b) $\sqrt{484} - \sqrt{361}$

.... [2]

4 Hard The area of a square is given by the following formula:

$A = S^2$ (where A = area and S = side length)

Calculate the side lengths of the squares with the following areas.
Give your answers to 1 decimal place.

a) 214 cm²

.... cm [1]

b) 8654 m²

.... m [1]

Score: [   ] out of **12**

Section 2 — Algebra and Graphs

Algebra

1 (Trickier)   Simplify the following:

    a) $x + x + x + 2$

    .... **[1]**

    b) $3a \times a \times b$

    .... **[1]**

2 (Trickier)   Simplify the expressions below:

    a) $5x - 6y + 3x$

    .... **[1]**

    b) $7x - 4y + 2x - 1 - 3y$

    .... **[1]**

3 (Hard)   Multiply out the brackets:

    a) $6(x + 2)$

    .... **[1]**

    b) $a(a - 1)$

    .... **[1]**

4 (Hard)   Expand $x(2x + 3) + y(y + 1) + 3(2x + y)$. Simplify fully your answer.

    .... **[2]**

5 (Hard)   The cost of a Blu-ray player is $(2x - 3)$ pounds and a television costs twice the price.

    a) Find an expression for the cost of the television.
       Multiply out your answer.

    .... **[2]**

    b) Find an expression for the cost of buying both a television and Blu-ray player.
       Simplify your answer.

    .... **[2]**

Score: [   ] out of **12**

Formulas

1 Easier To find Walter's age, you multiply Erik's age by 3 then add 4.

Erik is 13. How old is Walter?

....

[1]

2 Easier Substitute $x = 3$ into the expression $4x - 16$.

....

[1]

3 Trickier The formula for the time in minutes, T, required to cook a turkey that weighs W kilograms is:

$$T = \frac{155W + 400}{5}$$

Find the time required to cook a 4 kg turkey.

.... minutes

[2]

4 Trickier A famous formula by Isaac Newton is shown below.

$$F = ma$$

Find the value of F when $m = 45$ and $a = 8$. Show your working.

....

[1]

5 Trickier The formula below is used to convert degrees Fahrenheit, F, into degrees Celsius, C.

Convert 122 °F into °C.

$$C = \frac{5(F - 32)}{9}$$

.... °C

[1]

Score: ☐ **out of 6**

Making Formulas From Words

1 Trickier

Shappi thinks of a number, N. She divides it by three and then subtracts four to get P.

Which of the formulas below gives the value of P? Circle the correct answer.

$$P = \frac{N - 4}{3} \qquad\qquad P = 3N + 4 \qquad\qquad P = 3(N - 4) \qquad\qquad P = \frac{N}{3} - 4$$

[1]

2 Trickier

Helen runs some stables.
A name-plate for a stable door costs £20 plus £1 for every letter in the horse's name.

Write down a formula for the cost C (in pounds) for a name-plate with n letters on it.

....

[1]

3 Hard

David says "To find Y, you square X, then multiply by four and then add three."

Write down a formula for Y in terms of X.

....

[2]

4 Hard

A gardener charges £x per hour and works for h hours a day for five days a week.

What is her weekly wage in terms of x and h?

....

[1]

5 Hard

Raj won £W in a lottery. He donated £50 000 of his winnings to charity, and divided the remaining money between his three children.

Find a formula that gives the amount, A, that each of the children received in terms of W.

....

[2]

Score: [ ] out of **7**

Solving Equations

1 Find the values of *x* and *y*.

Trickier

a) $x + 6 = 9$

$x = $ .... [1]

b) $y - 3 = 2$

$y = $ .... [1]

2 Solve the equations below.

Trickier

a) $7a = 21$

$a = $ .... [1]

b) $\dfrac{b}{3} = 15$

$b = $ .... [1]

3 Find solutions to these equations:

Trickier

a) $m + 7 = 2$

$m = $ .... [1]

b) $-\dfrac{n}{5} = -1$

$n = $ .... [1]

4 Jamil is told that $19x - 7 = 6$.
What is the value of $19x + 3$?

Trickier

.... [1]

5 Given that $3x = 5$, what is the value of $12x$?

Trickier

.... [1]

Section 2 — Algebra and Graphs

Solving Equations

6 (Hard) Find solutions to the following equations. Show your working.

a) $2s + 1 = 5$

$s =$ ....
[2]

b) $3r - 5 = 4$

$r =$ ....
[2]

7 (Hard) Follow the steps below to solve $2(x + 3) = 4$.

a) Expand $2(x + 3)$.

....
[1]

b) Use your answer to part a) to help you solve $2(x + 3) = 4$. Show your working.

$x =$ ....
[2]

8 (Hard) Solve the equation $2x + 8 = 4 - 6x$.

$x =$ ....
[2]

9 (Hard) Harry's room is rectangular, and has walls of length $2x$ and $x + 3$ metres.

2x

x + 3

a) Given that Harry's room has a perimeter of 18 metres,
write an equation in the form $ax + b = c$ for the perimeter of Harry's room.

....
[1]

b) Solve your equation to find the value of x.

$x =$ ....
[2]

Score: ☐ out of **20**

Number Patterns and Sequences

1 😀 Easier In each part below a rule is given for finding the terms in a sequence. Find the next three terms in each case.

a) Add 6 on to the previous term.

3, ... , ... , ...

[1]

b) Multiply the previous term by 3.

1, ... , ... , ...

[1]

2 😀 Easier The rule for a sequence is "double the previous term and subtract 3". Use this rule to write the next four terms if the first term is 4.

4, ... , ... , ... , ...

[2]

3 😀 Easier A sequence starts 5, 12, 19, 26.

What is the rule to find the next term in the sequence?

....

[1]

4 😀 Trickier Here is a pattern sequence:

1st   2nd   3rd   4th

a) Draw the 4th pattern in the sequence.

[1]

b) How many dots will there be in the 5th pattern?

....

[1]

5 😀 Trickier A sequence has n^{th} term $4n - 2$.

Remember, n is the position of the term in the sequence.

Write down the first 3 terms of the sequence

.... , ... , ...

[1]

Number Patterns and Sequences

6 Trickier — Jess writes down a sequence with n^{th} term $3n - 5$.

What is the 15th term in the sequence?

.... [1]

7 Hard — Ruth is using tiles to make a pattern.

1st   2nd   3rd   4th

The number of white tiles in the nth pattern is n.
The number of grey tiles in the nth pattern is $2n - 1$.
How many tiles are there in total in the 27th term?

.... [2]

8 Hard — Find the nth term of the following sequence:

8, 10, 12, 14, ...

n^{th} term = ... [2]

9 Hard — Jasmine writes down the following sequence:

4, 1, -2, -5, -8, ...

a) Find the nth term of the sequence.

n^{th} term = ... [2]

b) What is the 20th term in the sequence?

.... [1]

Score: ☐ out of **16**

X and Y Coordinates

1 😊
Easier

Points A, B and C are plotted on the axes below.

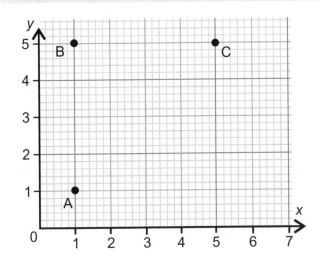

a) Write down the coordinates of points A, B and C.

A (............. , ...)

B (............. , ...)

C (............. , ...)

[3]

b) Plot the point D on the grid so that ABCD is a square.

[1]

c) Draw in the diagonals of the square.
Write down the coordinates of the point where the diagonals cross.

(............. , ...)

[1]

2 😊
Trickier

Here is a set of axes on a grid:

a) On the grid, plot the points: P (–2, 3)   Q (3, 3)   R (3, 0)   S (–2, –3)

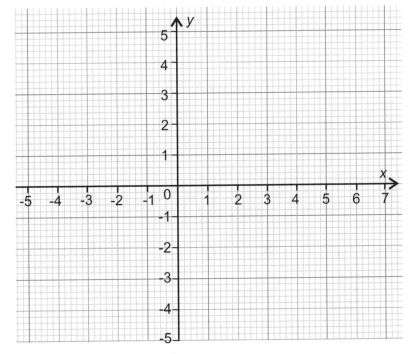

[2]

b) Join up the points to create shape PQRS. What is the mathematical name of this shape?

....

[1]

Score: [   ] out of **8**

Straight Line Graphs

1 😟 Hard   Answer the following questions using the grid below.

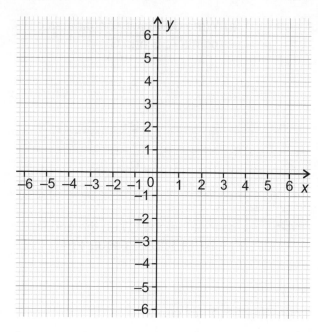

a) On the grid draw the following lines:

    i) $x = 5$

    ii) $y = -2$

    iii) $y = x$

                                            [3]

b) Write down the coordinates of the point where the lines $x = 5$ and $y = x$ meet.

            (.............. , ...)

                                                      [1]

c) What sort of triangle have the three lines made?

            ....

                                                     [1]

2 😟 Hard   There are three lines drawn on the axes below.

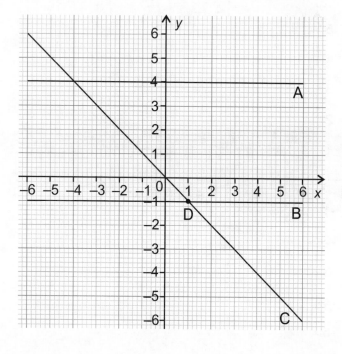

a) Write down the equation of the line labelled A.

            ....

                                                     [1]

b) Write down the equation of the line labelled B.

            ....

                                                      [1]

c) Write down the equation of the line labelled C.

            ....

                                                      [1]

d) Write down the coordinates of the point labelled D.

            (.............. , ...)

                                                        [1]

Score: [   ] out of **9**

Plotting Straight Line Graphs

1 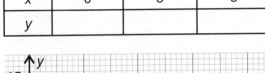 The graph of $y = 3x - 2$ is a straight line.

a) Complete this table of values for the equation $y = 3x - 2$.

x	0	3	5
y			

[1]

b) Plot the graph of $y = 3x - 2$ on the axes below.

[1]

c) Write down the point of intersection of the line $y = 3x - 2$ with the x-axis.

....

[1]

2 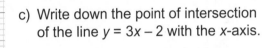 The graph of $x + y = 4$ is a straight line.

a) The equation $x + y = 4$ can be written in a different way. Tick the correct way below.

☐ $x = y + 4$ ☐ $y = x + 4$ ☐ $x = y - 4$ ☐ $y = 4 - x$

[1]

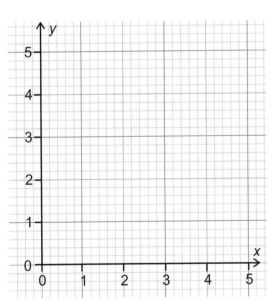

b) Complete the table of values below for the equation $x + y = 4$.

x	0	2	4
y			

[1]

c) Use your table of values to plot the graph of $x + y = 4$ on the axes on the left.

[1]

Score: ☐ out of **6**

Real-Life Graphs

1 😊 *Trickier*   Use this conversion graph to help you answer the questions below.

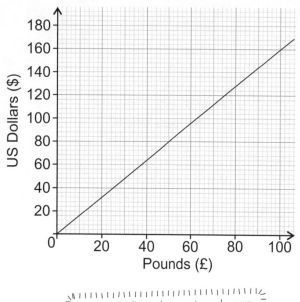

Ali is going shopping at an American store that only accepts dollars.

a) She gets £80 converted into dollars. How many dollars does this give her?

$ .... [1]

b) She spends $80 then gets the remaining money converted back into pounds. How much money does she have left?

Look carefully at the axes to make sure you're reading values off the correct one.

£ .... [2]

2 😟 *Hard*   The graph shows a journey of a van starting at Town A, travelling to Town B which is 50 miles away, and returning to Town A.

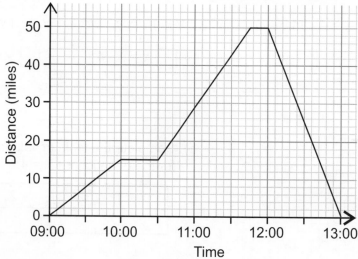

a) For how long was the van stationary during the journey?

.... minutes [1]

b) How far did the van travel before it stopped for the first time?

.... miles [1]

c) Between what times was the van travelling at its fastest speed?

.... [1]

Score: ☐ out of **6**

Ratios

1 😛 Simplify fully the following ratios.
Trickier

a) 5 : 15

.... [1]

b) £7 : £49

.... [1]

c) 28 cm : 8 cm

.... [1]

2 😛 In an office, the ratio of printers to computers is 2 : 9.
Trickier

a) There are 45 computers in the office. How many printers are there?

.... [1]

b) There are 3 photocopiers in the office.
Give the ratio of computers to photocopiers in its simplest form.

.... [1]

3 😀 Kate and Deborah share £3600 in the ratio 4 : 5.
Hard

How much money does each person get?

Add up your answers to check you get back to the total amount, £3600.

Kate gets £................... and Deborah gets £...................

[3]

4 😀 Sam is 6 years old. Ed is three years older than Sam.
Hard
Sam and Ed share a bag of 45 sweets in the ratio of their ages.

How many sweets does Ed get?

.... [3]

Score: ☐ out of **11**

Proportion Problems

1 Trickier Dr Williamson is buying some stationery for his surgery.

   a) 5 notebooks cost £10.80. Find the cost of 3 notebooks.

   .... [2]

   b) 15 pens cost £11.25. Find the cost of 34 pens.

   .... [2]

2 Trickier 5 call centre workers can make 40 phone calls per hour.

   a) How many calls could 5 call centre workers make in 4 hours?

   .... [1]

   b) How many calls per hour could 8 call centre workers make?

   .... [2]

3 Hard Trevor is making some sachets of curry powder from the recipe below:

Curry Power (6 sachets)
30 g ground cumin
30 g ground coriander
9 g ground turmeric
4 g cayenne pepper
11 g ground ginger

   a) Trevor wants to make 20 sachets.

   i) How much ground cumin will he need?

   .... g [2]

   ii) How much will 20 sachets of curry powder weigh?

   .... g [2]

   b) Trevor only has 15 g of ground turmeric left.
   What is the maximum number of sachets he can make?

   .... [2]

Proportion Problems

4 Hard Football stickers are available in packs of 5, 20 or 50.

A pack of 5 stickers costs 40p, a pack of 20 stickers costs £1.20 and a pack of 50 stickers costs £3.50.

Find the pack that represents the best value for money.

....
[3]

5 Hard A supermarket sells bottles of milk in three different sizes.

> A: 2 pint bottle at 96p
>
> B: 4 pint bottle at £1.72
>
> C: 6 pint bottle at £2.52

Which bottle of milk represents the best value for money?

....
[3]

6 Hard A cheese shop sells two different brands of cheddar cheese.

> Cheddar & Sons
> £3.60 per 400 g pack

> Cheesetastic Cheddar
> £9.40 per 1 kg pack

a) Which cheese gives the better value for money?

....
[2]

b) How much would 6 kg of the best value cheese cost?

....
[2]

Score: [ ] out of **23**

Percentage Increase and Decrease

1 😕 Hard   Cashin's department store discounts 10% off all prices in the summer sale.
Work out the sale price of the following items:

a) A jumper costing £20.

....
[1]

b) A bottle of perfume costing £18.

....
[1]

2 😕 Hard   Cheapstuff recorded the number of shoppers visiting the store over two days.
On the first day there were 580 shoppers. On the second there were 25% more.

How many shoppers visited the store on the second day?

....
[1]

3 😕 Hard   Sammie and Joel invest their money with the Grabitall Bank.

Sammie invests £320 in an account that pays 4% simple interest each year.

Joel invests £420 in an account that pays 3% simple interest each year.

a) Who earns the most interest each year? Show your working.

....
[2]

b) How much money will Joel have after 5 years?

Make sure you give the total
and not just the interest.

....
[2]

Score: ⬜ out of **7**

Conversion Factors

1 😃 Easier Pete took his pet salamander to the vet to get it weighed and measured.

a) The salamander weighed 374 g. Give the salamander's weight in kg.

.... kg
[1]

b) The salamander was 20.2 cm long. Give the salamander's length in mm.

.... mm
[1]

2 😃 Easier A cricket pitch is 22 yards long.

a) Give the length of a cricket pitch in feet.

.... ft
[1]

b) Using your answer to part a), find the length of a cricket pitch in inches.

.... inches
[1]

3 😛 Trickier Mr Evy attends his local slimming club. Since starting he has lost a total of 33 lb.

a) How many kilograms is this?

.... kg
[1]

b) He needs to lose another 44 lb to achieve his target weight.
   What will his total weight loss be in stones?

.... stones
[2]

4 😛 Trickier Mr Roe is buying a new car and he wants to compare the different petrol tank sizes.

	Tank A	Tank B	Tank C
Petrol Tank Size	12 gallons	56 litres	52000 cm^3

Which tank is the biggest? Show your working.

....
[2]

Score: .... out of **9**

Time and Timetables

1 😊 A coach journey departs at 15:20 and arrives at 19:05.
Easier

a) Write the departure and arrival times in the 12-hour clock.

departure time: .... arrival time: ....

[2]

b) How long does the coach journey last?

.... hours and .... minutes

[1]

2 😊 A film starts at 7:30 pm and lasts 1 hour and 50 minutes.
Easier

a) What is the length of the film in minutes?

.... minutes

[1]

b) What time does the film finish? Give your answer in the 24-hour clock.

....

[2]

3 😐 This is part of a bus timetable.
Trickier

Acacia Avenue	12:46	13:01	13:16	13:31
English Street	12:58	13:13	13:28	13:43
Market Square	13:03	13:18	13:33	13:48
Railway Station	13:13	13:28	13:43	13:58
Bus Station	13:17	13:32	13:47	14:02

a) A bus leaves Acacia Avenue at 13:16.
Write this time in the 12-hour clock.

....

[1]

b) If you arrive at the Market Square at 1:20 pm,
how long do you have to wait for the next bus?

.... minutes

[1]

c) What is the time of the latest bus leaving English Street that will get you to
the bus station before 2:00 pm? Give your answer in the 12-hour clock.

....

[1]

Score: ☐ out of **9**

Maps and Scale Drawings

1 😊 The map shows the position of some tourist attractions on CGP island.
Trickier The scale of the map is 1 cm = 4 km.

a) Work out the real-life distance between the Banyan Tree and the Castle.

.... km

[2]

b) Work out the real-life distance from Misty Mountain to the Hidden Caves.

.... km

[2]

c) Treasure is buried 12 km west of the Waterfall. Mark the position of the treasure on the map.

[2]

2 😊 Alan has made a scale drawing of his living room using the scale 1 : 100.
Trickier

What is the real-life length of the longest side of his rug? Give your answer in metres.

.... m

[2]

3 😊 A shop sells model vehicles that are made to the scale of 1 : 50.
Trickier

a) A model car is 9 cm long. What is the length, in cm, of the car in real life?

.... cm

[1]

b) A bus is 11 m long in real life. How long, in cm, would a model of the bus be?

.... cm

[2]

Score: [   ] out of **11**

Speed

1 😖 Hard — Calculate the speed of each of these animals. Give appropriate units with your answers.

a) A donkey that travelled 12 km in 3 hours.

.... [1]

b) A goose that swam 20 metres in 40 seconds.

.... [1]

2 😖 Hard — Find the distance travelled by a bus going at an average speed of 50 km/h from 8 am till 11 am.

.... km [2]

3 😖 Hard — A horse-drawn carriage travels at an average speed of 9.6 km/h.

a) How far will it travel in 3 hours?

.... km [1]

b) A golf buggy travels at an average speed of 10.8 km/h. How much further will it travel in 3 hours than the horse-drawn carriage?

.... km [2]

4 😖 Hard — Ben travelled by car from his house to the airport. The airport is 180 miles away from his house and he drove at an average speed of 40 mph.

If Ben left his house at 11 am, what time did he get to the airport?

.... [2]

Score: ☐ out of **9**

Section 3 — Ratio, Proportion and Rates of Change

Symmetry

1 😀 Which of the letters below have:
Easier

ROSE

a) 2 lines of symmetry?

.... [1]

b) rotational symmetry of order 2?

.... [1]

c) 1 line of symmetry?

.... [1]

2 😀 Look at the shape below.
Easier

a) Draw all of the lines of symmetry on the shape.

[1]

b) What is the order of rotational symmetry of this shape?

.... [1]

3 😀 Draw in the necessary lines to make each of the
Easier shapes below have rotational symmetry of order 4.

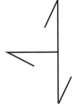  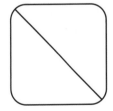

[3]

Score: ☐ out of **8**

2D Shapes

1 😊 *Easier*   Draw lines to join each shape to its correct label.

Rhombus   Trapezium   Rectangle   Parallelogram

[2]

2 😊 *Easier*   Fill in the missing numbers.

a) A kite has .... pairs of sides of equal length.

It has .... line(s) of symmetry and rotational symmetry of order ....

[3]

b) An isosceles triangle has .... equal sides and .... line(s) of symmetry.

[2]

3 😊 *Easier*   Complete this table about triangles:

Type of Triangle	Equilateral triangle		
Diagram			
Number of equal angles			0

[3]

4 😟 *Trickier*   A right-angled triangle has one line of symmetry. What are its three angles?

.... , ... , ...

[2]

Score: ☐ out of **12**

Regular Polygons

1 😃 Five shapes are drawn below.
Easier

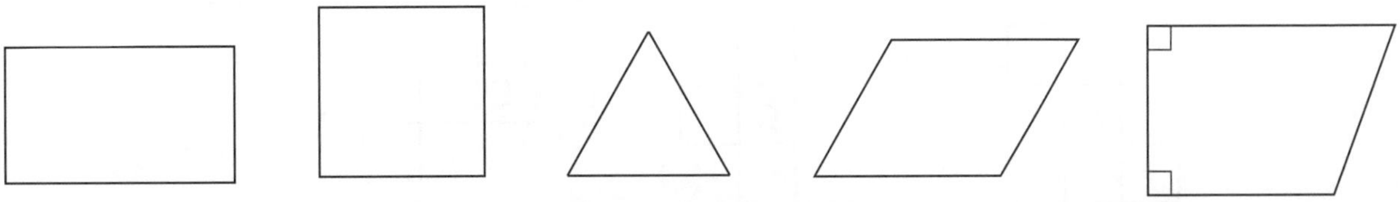

Rectangle   Square   Equilateral Triangle   Parallelogram   Trapezium

State which of the shapes are regular.

....

[1]

2 😃 This shape is a regular pentagon.
Easier

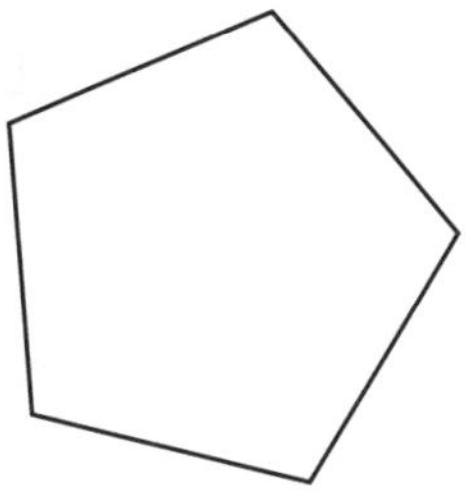

a) Draw all the lines of symmetry on the pentagon.
   You may use a mirror or tracing paper to help you.

[1]

b) What is the order of rotational symmetry of a regular pentagon?

....

[1]

3 😃 Here is a regular polygon.
Easier

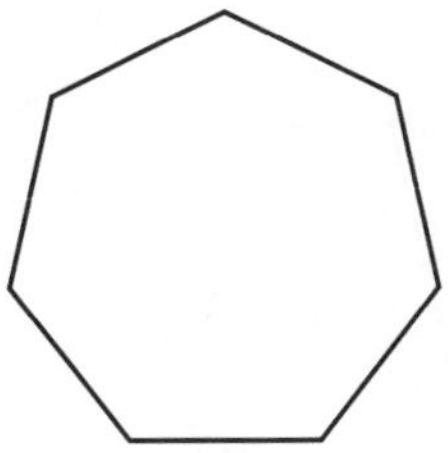

a) What is the name of this shape?   ....

[1]

b) How many lines of symmetry does it have?

....

[1]

c) What is its order of rotational symmetry?

....

[1]

Score: ☐ out of **6**

Congruence and Similarity

1 Trickier — Write down the letters of the shapes that are congruent to shape A.

.... [2]

2 Trickier — How many of these shapes are similar?

Number of similar shapes = ... [1]

Score: ☐ out of **3**

Perimeter

1 😃 Easier   The diagram below shows a piece of paper.

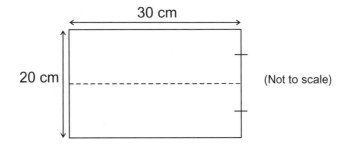

30 cm

20 cm

(Not to scale)

a) What is the perimeter of the sheet of paper?

.... cm
[1]

b) If I cut the paper in half along the dotted line,
what is the perimeter of one of the smaller rectangles?

.... cm
[2]

2 😕 Trickier   The perimeter of this triangle is 24 cm.
What are the missing lengths?

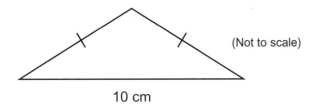

(Not to scale)

10 cm

.... cm , ... cm
[2]

3 😃 Trickier   Use the axes given below for this question.

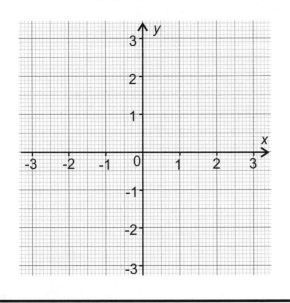

a) Plot these coordinates and join the points
in order to make a pentagon.

(2, 0)   (0, –2)   (–2, –2)   (–2, 2)   (2, 3)
[2]

b) What is the perimeter of the pentagon?
Give your answer in mm.

.... mm
[2]

Score: ☐ out of **9**

Area

1 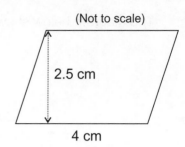 Find the area of this parallelogram, stating the units in your answer.

(Not to scale)

2.5 cm

4 cm

.... [1]

2 The diagram below shows a trapezium.

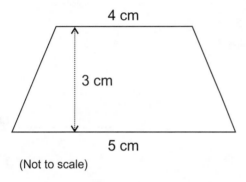

4 cm

3 cm

5 cm

(Not to scale)

a) Explain how to find the area of a trapezium.

....

....

....
[1]

b) What is the area of this trapezium?

.... cm² [2]

3 The length of a rectangle is 6 cm and its area is 21 cm².

What is the width of this rectangle?

.... cm [1]

4 Find the area of this triangle.

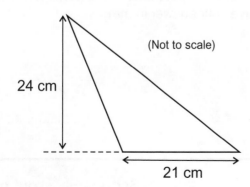

(Not to scale)

24 cm

21 cm

.... cm² [2]

Area

5 (Hard) Look at the diagram of a flower bed shown below:

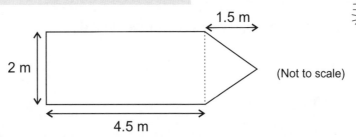

Split the shape into shapes you know.

(Not to scale)

What is the area of the flower bed? Show all your working.

.... m²

[2]

6 (Hard) Find the area of this T shape.

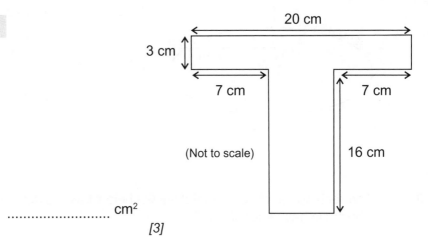

(Not to scale)

.... cm²

[3]

7 (Hard) Which shape has the larger area — the rectangle or the rhombus?

Show all your working.

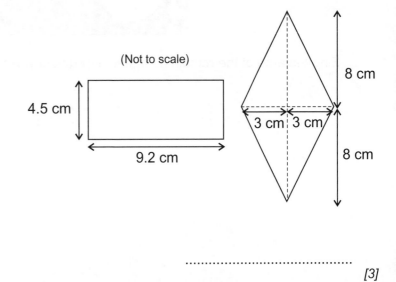

(Not to scale)

....

[3]

Score: ☐ out of **15**

Circles

1 😟 *Hard*   A circular table top has a diameter of 80 cm.

Find the area of the table top, giving your answer to 2 d.p.

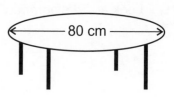

.... cm²

[2]

2 😟 *Hard*   The Andersons want to build a circular pond in their garden.
They mark out the rim of the pond using a stake pushed into the ground
and a taut piece of string with a length of 1.6 m, as shown.

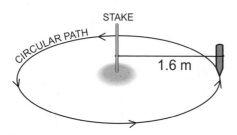

What will be the circumference of their pond?
Give your answer to 2 d.p.

.... m

[2]

3 😟 *Hard*   The rectangular sheet of metal shown below has a circle cut out of it.
The circle has radius, R, of 3 cm.

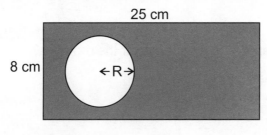

(Not to scale)

Find the area of the remaining metal, giving your answer to 2 d.p.

.... cm²

[3]

Score: ☐ out of **7**

3D Shapes

1 🙂 Easier Fill in the missing words.

a) A triangle-based pyramid is called a ....

[1]

b) A prism with a cross-section in the shape of a rectangle is a ....

[1]

c) The mathematical name for a ball is a ....

[1]

2 🙂 Easier Give the full names of the following three solids.

a)   b)   c)

a) ....

[1]

b) ....

[1]

c) ....

[1]

3 🙂 Easier A square-based pyramid is glued to fit exactly on top of a cuboid.

a) How many vertices does the square-based pyramid have?

....

[1]

b) How many vertices does the cuboid have?

....

[1]

c) How many vertices will the new solid have?

....

[1]

Score: [   ] out of **9**

Nets and Surface Area

1 🙂 Look at these diagrams. Tick the box below each net that will fold up to make a cube.
Easier

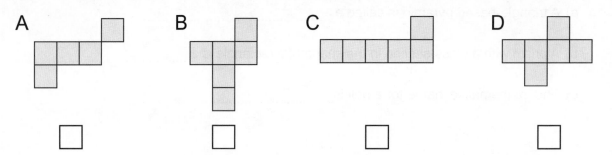

A   B   C   D

☐   ☐   ☐   ☐

[2]

2 🙂 Write down the names of the 3D shapes shown by the nets below.
Easier

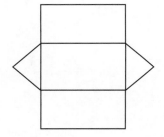   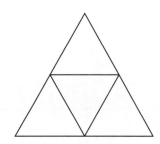

....

[2]

3 🙂 This is a net of a cuboid.
Easier

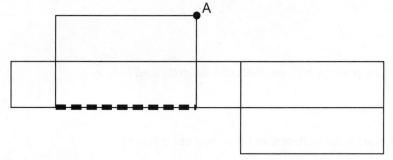

a) Mark the point on the net which will meet corner A
   when the net is folded to form a cuboid. Label it B.

[1]

b) Draw a bold line to show which edge will meet the dotted line
   when the net is folded into a cuboid.

[1]

Nets and Surface Area

4 Trickier   The diagram on the right shows a cuboid.

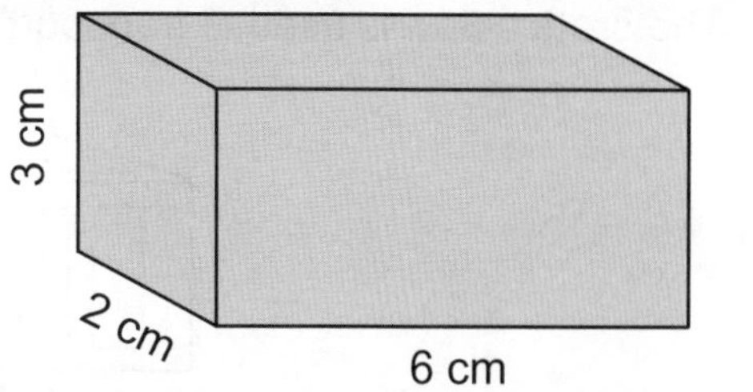

   a) Sketch the net of the cuboid and label it with
      the dimensions of each part of the net.

3 cm

2 cm

6 cm

(Not to scale)

[2]

   b) Use your net to find the total surface area of the cuboid.

.... cm²

[2]

5 Hard   All four side faces of the square-based pyramid below are isosceles triangles.

   a) Sketch a net of the solid and label it with
      the appropriate measurements.

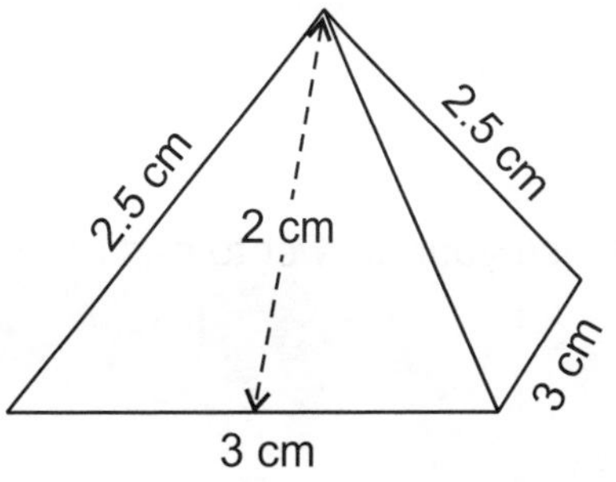

2.5 cm

2.5 cm

2 cm

3 cm

3 cm

(Not to scale)

[2]

   b) What is the surface area of the square-based pyramid?

.... cm²

[2]

Score: ☐ out of **14**

Volume

1 😊 Easier The crate below is used to transport car parts all over the world. It is cuboid-shaped.

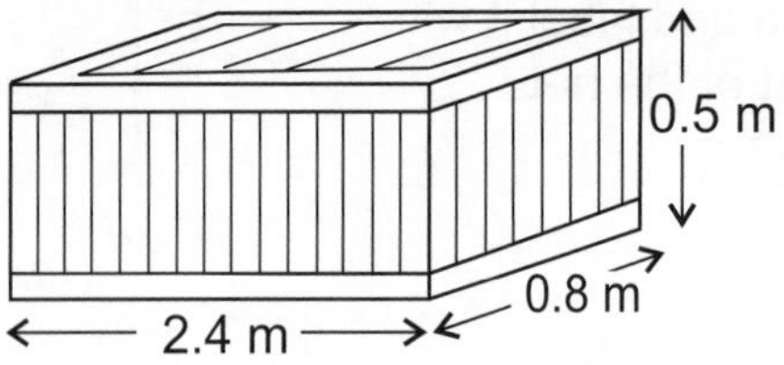

0.5 m

(Not to scale)

2.4 m 0.8 m

Find the volume of the crate.

.... m³

[1]

2 😵 Trickier The diagram below shows a triangular prism.

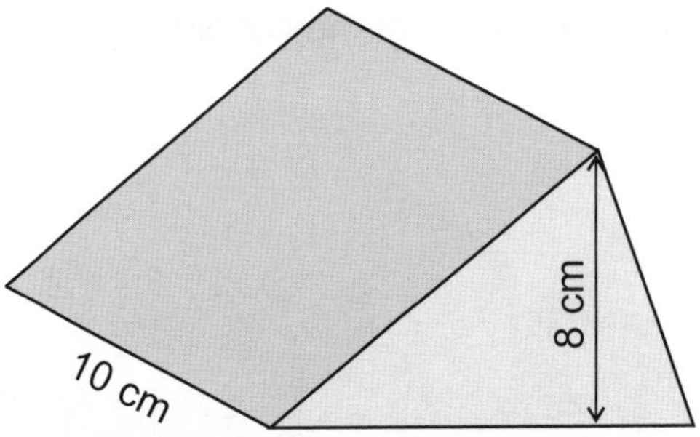

10 cm

8 cm

11 cm

(Not to scale)

a) Find the area of the cross-section of the prism.

.... cm²

[1]

b) Use your answer to part a) to find the volume of the prism.

.... cm³

[1]

3 😟 Hard The cross-section of a tin of baked beans is a circle with a radius of 3.7 cm.

You'll need to use the formula for area of a circle.

a) Find the area of the cross-section. Give your answer to 2 d.p.

.... cm²

[1]

b) The tin is 11 cm high. What is its volume? Give your answer to 2 d.p.

.... cm³

[1]

Score: out of **5**

Lines and Angles

1 The diagram below is drawn on squared paper.

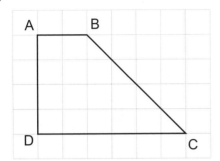

Write down the sizes of the following angles:

DAB = ...

BCD = ...

[2]

2 Look at the angles *a* and *b* shown below.

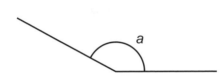 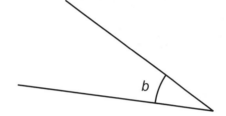

a) What type of angle is:

   i) angle *a*? ....   ii) angle *b*? ....

[2]

b) Measure the size of each angle.

   i) angle *a* = ...   ii) angle *b* = ...

[2]

3 Use a protractor to draw these angles, using the base lines given.

a) 35°   b) 145°

[2]

Score: [ ] out of **8**

Angle Rules

1 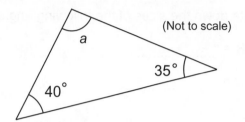 Trickier Find the size of each of these angles.

(Not to scale)

a

35°

40°

a = ...

[1]

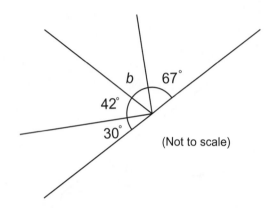

b 67°

42°

30°

(Not to scale)

b = ...

[1]

2 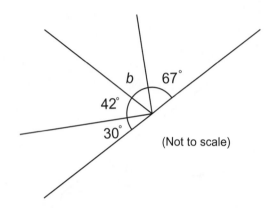 Trickier Work out the size of each of these angles.

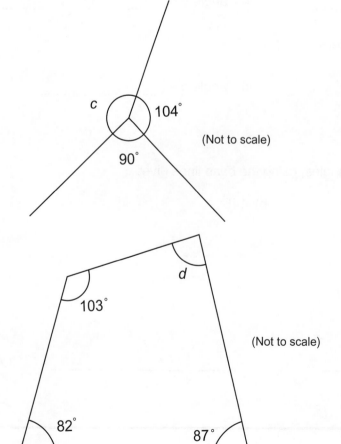

c

104°

(Not to scale)

90°

c = ...

[1]

d

103°

(Not to scale)

82°

87°

d = ...

[1]

Angle Rules

3 Trickier   Find the size of angle *a*.

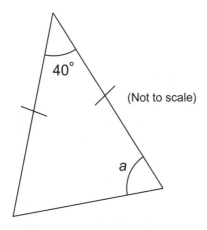

(Not to scale)

a = ...

[2]

4 Trickier   Find the size of angles *b* and *c*.

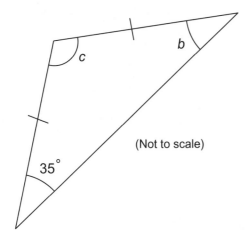

(Not to scale)

b = ...

[1]

c = ...

[1]

5 Hard   Calculate the size of angle *d*.

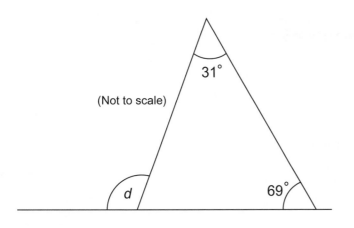

(Not to scale)

d = ...

[2]

Score: ☐ out of **10**

Parallel Lines

1 😖 Hard

Find angles *a* and *b* in the diagram below.

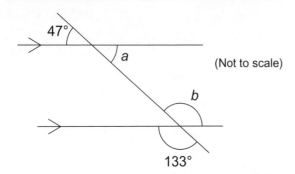

47°

a

(Not to scale)

b

133°

a = ...

b = ...

[2]

2 😖 Hard

Find the missing angles in the diagram below.

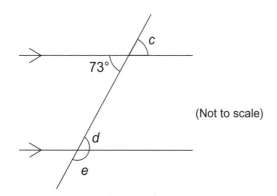

c

73°

(Not to scale)

d

e

c = ...

d = ...

e = ...

[3]

3 😖 Hard

Find angles *f* and *g* in the diagram below.

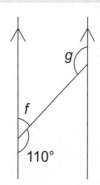

g

f

110°

(Not to scale)

f = ...

g = ...

[2]

4 😖 Hard

Calculate angles *h*, *i* and *j* in the diagram below.

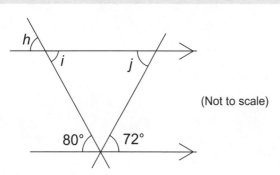

h

i

j

80°

72°

(Not to scale)

h = ...

i = ...

j = ...

[3]

Score: out of **10**

Interior and Exterior Angles

1 😟
Hard
A 50 pence piece is based on a regular heptagon.

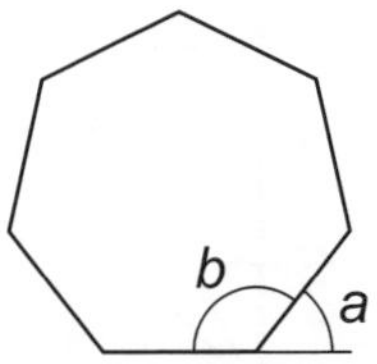

a) Calculate the exterior angle marked *a*, to 1 decimal place.

....
[1]

b) Calculate the interior angle marked *b*, to 1 decimal place.

....
[1]

c) Calculate the sum of all seven interior angles.

....
[1]

2 😟
Hard
Joe draws a 20-sided polygon.

Find the sum of the interior angles in a 20 sided polygon.

....
[2]

3 😟
Hard
The diagram below shows an irregular hexagon.

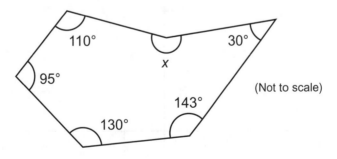

110°   30°

x

95°

(Not to scale)

143°

130°

Find the size of angle *x*.

....
[3]

Score: [   ] out of **8**

Translations

1 😟 Trickier — The diagram shows three triangles A, B and C on a coordinate grid.

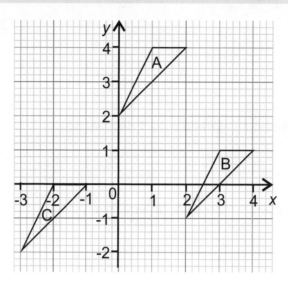

Find the vector for the translation that maps:

a) A to C

....

b) C to B

....

[2]

2 😐 Trickier — Triangle ABC is drawn on the coordinate grid below.

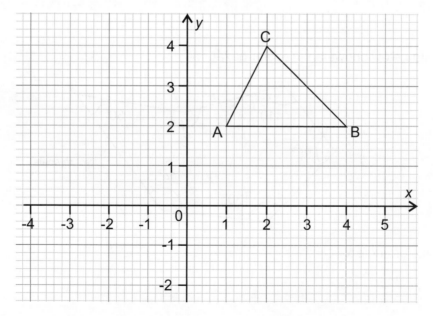

Translate triangle ABC by the vector $\begin{pmatrix} -5 \\ -1 \end{pmatrix}$. Label the image $A_1B_1C_1$.

[2]

Score: ☐ out of **4**

Reflections

1 🙂 Easier Reflect this shape in the mirror line.

You may use a mirror or
tracing paper to help you.

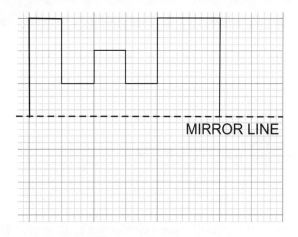

MIRROR LINE

[1]

2 🙂 Easier In the diagram below, shape A is a reflection of shape B. Draw in the mirror line.

You may use a mirror or tracing paper to help you.

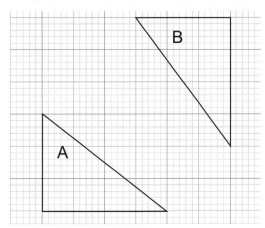

[1]

3 🙂 Trickier Draw the reflection of the shape in the line $y = x$.

You may use a mirror or tracing paper to help you.

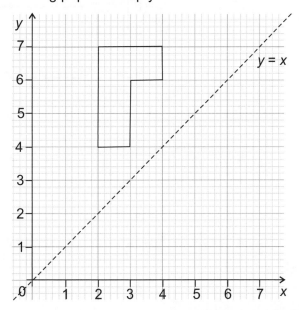

[1]

Score: ☐ out of **3**

Rotations

1 😊
Easier

The shaded rectangle is rotated as shown so that point A stays in the same place.

Mark on the diagram the new position of point B.

[1]

You can use tracing paper to help you with rotation questions.

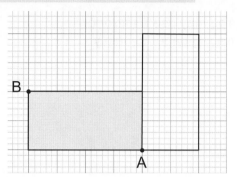

2 😛
Trickier

Shape A can be rotated clockwise onto shape B.

a) Draw a cross to show the centre of rotation.

[1]

b) What is the angle of rotation?

.... *[1]*

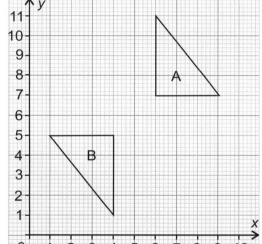

3 😛
Trickier

Draw this shape rotated 90° anticlockwise about the origin.

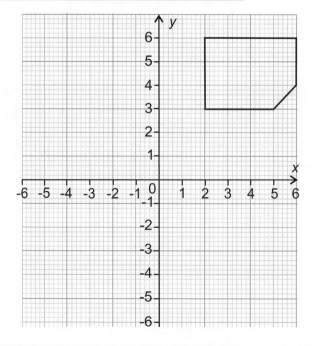

[2]

Score: [   ] out of **5**

Enlargements

1 😶 **Trickier** Enlarge this shape by a scale factor of 2.

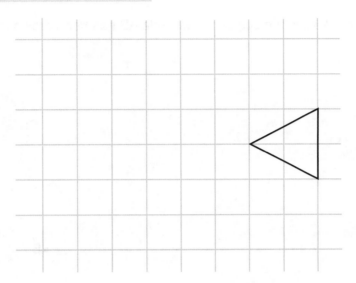

[1]

2 🙂 **Hard** The coordinate grid below shows an enlargement of shape A, labelled B.

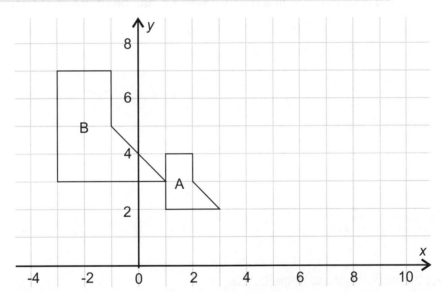

a) For the enlargement that maps shape A onto shape B, find:

   i) the scale factor

   .... *[1]*

   ii) the centre of enlargement

   .... *[1]*

b) Enlarge shape A by a scale factor of 3, using (0, 2) as the centre of enlargement.

[2]

Score: [ ] out of **5**

Constructions

1 Triangle ABC has sides AB = 7 cm, AC = 5 cm and BC = 6 cm.

Construct triangle ABC in the space below. Side AB has been drawn for you.

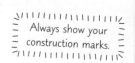
Always show your construction marks.

A ●————————————————● B

[2]

2 Triangle XYZ has side XY = 4 cm, side XZ = 6 cm and angle YXZ = 70°.

Construct triangle XYZ in the space below. Side XY has been drawn for you.

X
●

●
Y

[2]

3 Construct the bisector of the angle below.
Hard

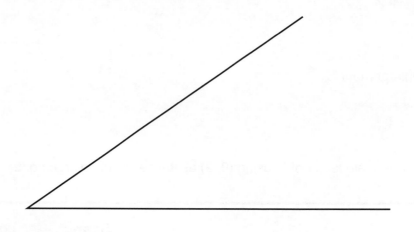

[2]

Section 4 — Geometry and Measures

Constructions

4 😵 Hard   Construct the perpendicular bisector of the line below.

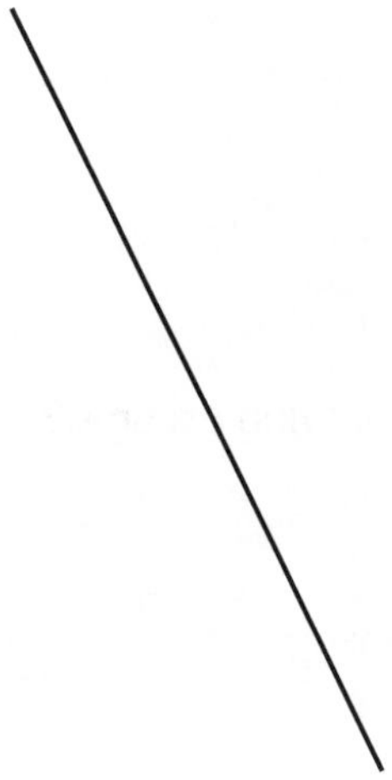

[2]

5 😵 Hard   The diagram below shows triangle ABC.

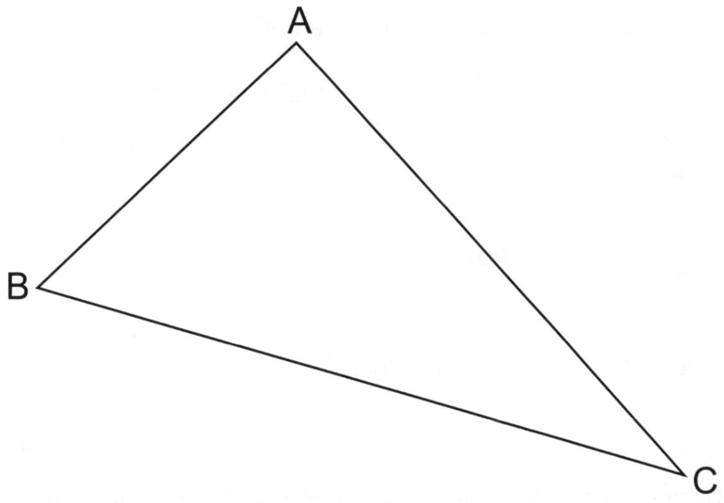

A

B

C

a) Construct the bisector of angle ACB.

[2]

b) Mark a point D on the triangle where the bisector drawn in a) crosses line AB.
How far is this point from B? Give your answer to the nearest mm.

.... mm

[1]

Score: ☐ out of **11**

Section 5 — Probability and Statistics

Probability

1 😃
Easier

Five friends regularly meet at 7 pm at the cinema to see a film.
The number line shows the probability of each friend arriving on time.

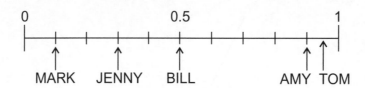

a) What is the probability of Jenny arriving on time?

....
[1]

b) Who is least likely to arrive on time?

....
[1]

c) Who is as likely to arrive late as on time?

....
[1]

2 😃
Easier

A box contains three types of solid: cubes, spheres and pyramids.
Each solid is either black, grey or white as shown below.

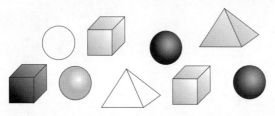

Kylie picks out a solid at random.

a) What is the probability that she takes
out a grey solid?

....
[1]

b) What is the probability that she takes out a cube?

....
[1]

c) What is the probability of her taking out a solid which is either white or grey?

....
[1]

3 😛
Trickier

The probability of a car having to stop at a set of traffic lights is $\frac{1}{5}$.
What is the probability that the car does not have to stop?

....
[1]

Probability

4 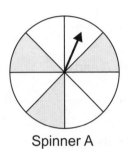 **Trickier** The two spinners below have been divided up into equal sections. Some sections of spinner A have been shaded.

 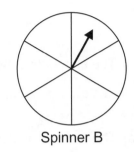

Spinner A   Spinner B

a) What is the probability of landing on a shaded section on spinner A?

.... [1]

b) Shade some sections of spinner B so that the probability of landing on an unshaded section is $\frac{2}{3}$.

[1]

5 **Hard** Below is a sample space diagram to show all the possible outcomes when a fair coin and fair six-sided dice are thrown together.

	1	2	3	4	5	6
Head (H)	H1					
Tail (T)					T5	

a) Complete the sample space diagram.

[1]

b) What is the probability of getting a tail and a 2?

.... [1]

c) What is the probability of getting a head and an even number?

.... [1]

6 **Hard** A bag contains 20 sweets, all of which are either lemon, lime or strawberry-flavoured. 6 of them are lemon-flavoured. The probability of picking a strawberry-flavoured one is $\frac{2}{5}$.

a) What is the probability of picking a lemon-flavoured sweet at random?

.... [1]

b) What is the probability of picking a lime-flavoured sweet at random?

.... [2]

Score: ☐ out of **15**

Venn Diagrams

1 😵 *Hard*   Using the Venn diagram below write down the following:

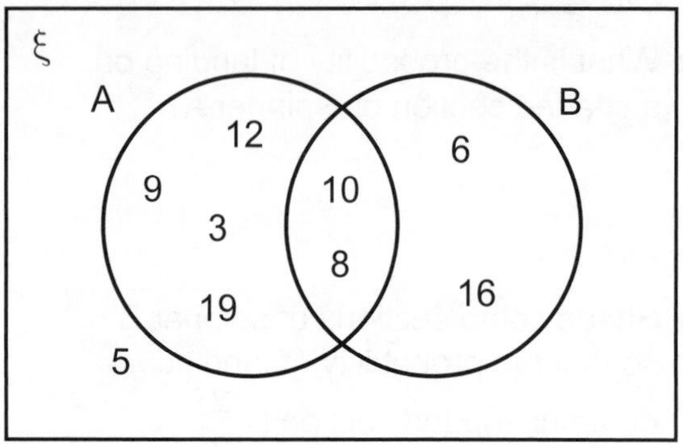

ξ

A   12   B

9   10

3

8

19   16

5

6

a) The elements of set B.

....

   [1]

b) The elements in **both** A and B.

....

   [1]

c) The number of elements in A.

....

   [1]

2 😵 *Hard*   A chip shop has two side dishes on the menu: mushy peas and gravy.
One evening, the shop owner recorded the choices that her customers made.
18 customers chose only mushy peas, 7 customers chose only gravy,
12 customers asked for both and 13 customers didn't want either.

Complete the Venn diagram to show this data.

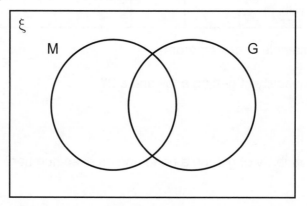

   [2]

3 😵 *Hard*   Let ξ = {whole numbers from 1 to 15}, P = {odd numbers} and Q = {multiples of 3}.

a) Complete the Venn diagram, showing the **number of elements** in each part of the diagram.

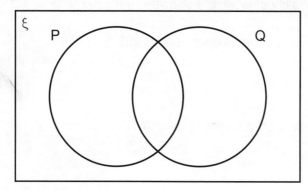

Writing out the elements of each set will help you work
out the number of elements in each part of the diagram.

   [3]

b) How many elements are **not** in set P?

....

   [1]

Score: ☐ out of **9**

Line Graphs and Pictograms

1 Easier The pictogram below shows the number of footballs sold by a sports shop on Saturdays in March.

Saturday 1st March ⚽ ⚽ ⚽ ◖

Saturday 8th March ⚽ ⚽

Saturday 15th March ⚽ ⚽ ⚽

Saturday 22nd March ⚽

Saturday 29th March

Key:
⚽ = 4 footballs

a) How many footballs were sold on 1st March?

....
[1]

b) On Saturday 29th March 16 footballs were sold. Complete the pictogram to show this data.

[1]

c) How many footballs were sold in total on Saturdays in March?

....
[1]

2 Trickier The table shows the number of pupils staying on at Tickem High School after Year 11. Each year, the school tries to encourage as many pupils as possible to stay on at school.

a) Draw a line graph on these axes to show the data below.

Year	Pupils
2009	100
2010	85
2011	105
2012	125
2013	110

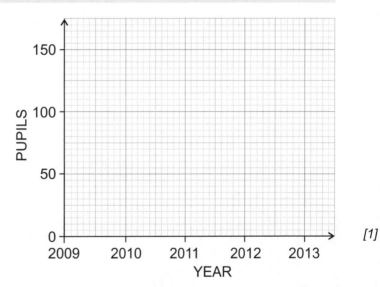

[1]

b) In which year did the most pupils stay on at Tickem High School? ....
[1]

c) Jenna says that the school must have done a very bad job of trying to get pupils to stay on at school in 2010. What other information do you need to tell if she is correct?

....

....

....
[1]

Score: ☐ out of **6**

Bar Charts

1 😊 Easier   A study has been carried out in a village asking people to name their favourite sport. The results are shown on the bar chart below.

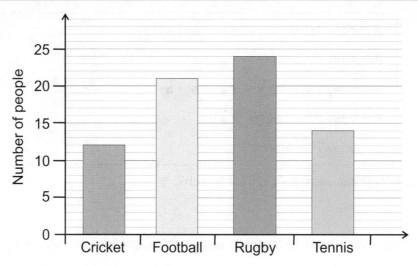

a) Which sport was chosen by 14 people?

.... [1]

b) How many people altogether chose football and cricket?

.... [1]

c) How many more people chose rugby than cricket?

.... [1]

2 😊 Easier   Pupils in Year 7 and 8 recorded how many portions of fruit they ate in a day. The information is shown in the dual bar chart below.

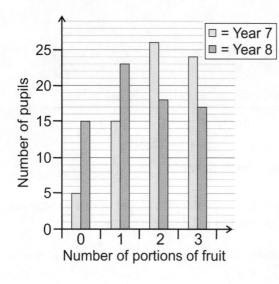

a) How many Year 8 pupils didn't eat any fruit?

.... [1]

b) How many pupils, in total, ate 3 portions of fruit?

.... [1]

c) What was the most common number of portions for pupils in Year 7?

.... [1]

d) How many **more** Year 8 pupils ate 1 portion than Year 7 pupils?

.... [1]

Score: _____ out of **7**

Pie Charts

1 Trickier

Three friends recorded the amount of time they spent reading, watching TV, and on a computer over a week. The pie charts show the proportion of their time that they spent on each activity:

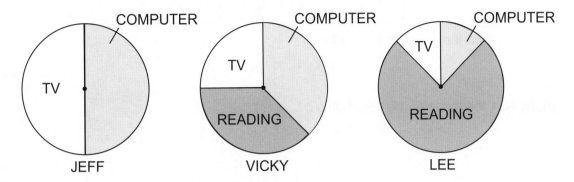

JEFF   VICKY   LEE

a) Who spent the highest proportion of their time reading? .... [1]

b) Who spent the smallest proportion of their time reading? .... [1]

c) Why can't we use the pie charts to say who spent the most time watching TV?

....

.... [1]

2 Hard

The table shows the number of hours Leanne spends each day on four activities.

a) Calculate the angles needed to draw a pie chart of this information.

Activity	Lessons	Meals	Homework	Hobbies
Time	5	3	1	3
Angle				

[2]

b) Complete the pie chart below.

Make sure your angles add up to 360°.

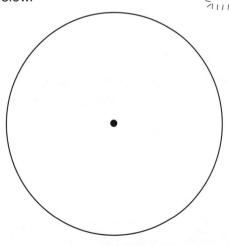

[2]

Score: [ ] out of **7**

Mean, Median, Mode and Range

1 Trickier Jenny sat twelve mental Maths tests in a term. She scored the following marks out of ten:

> 4, 7, 3, 1, 4, 6, 8, 4, 5, 7, 5, 6

a) Write down the range of the marks.

.... [1]

b) What is the mode of this set of data?

.... [1]

c) Calculate her mean mark.

.... [1]

2 Trickier Chris records the temperature (in °C) in his city every day for 1 week.

> 3, –3, 4, 0, –1, 2, 4

a) What is the mean temperature for these seven days? Give your answer to 2 d.p.

......................°C [1]

b) What is the median temperature?

......................°C [2]

3 Hard Russell took three tests. Each test was out of 20 marks.
He scored 14 and 16 in the first two. His mean score was 16 for the three tests overall.

What was Russell's mark in the third test?

Check your answer by using it, along with the two scores you know, to find the mean.

.... [1]

Score: [ ] out of **7**

Averages from Frequency Tables

1 😟 Hard · A class collected information about the number of pets in each of their families. This information was displayed in a frequency table.

Number of Pets	Number of Families	No. of Pets × No. of Families
0	2	
1	6	
2	8	
3	9	
4	2	
TOTAL		

a) Is the data shown in the table discrete or continuous?

....

[1]

b) Complete the table.

[2]

c) Find the mean number of pets per family. Give your answer to 1 d.p.

....

[1]

2 😟 Hard · A survey of the number of devices with Wi-Fi® in pupils' homes gave these results.

Number of devices	Frequency	Number of devices × Frequency
1	55	55
2	68	136
3	75	
4	25	
5	15	
6	8	
7	4	
TOTAL		

a) Complete the table.

[2]

b) Calculate the mean number of devices with Wi-Fi® to 1 d.p.

....

[1]

Score: ☐ out of **7**

Scatter Graphs

1 😟 Hard 5 siblings decide to plot their heights in metres against their ages.

Four of the family have plotted their data on the graph below.

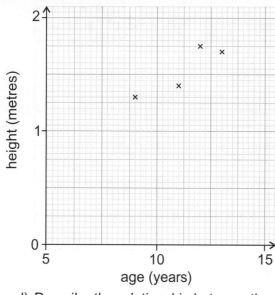

a) Becky is 13 years old. How tall is she?

.... m

[1]

b) Norman is 7 years old and is 1.1 m tall.
Plot Norman's height and age on the graph.

[1]

c) Add a line of best fit to this scatter graph.

[1]

d) Describe the relationship between the siblings' ages and their heights.

....

....

[1]

2 😟 Hard The graphs below show daily sales of 3 products at a snack stall plotted against temperature.

Graph A 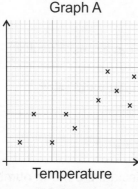   Graph B 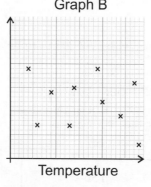   Graph C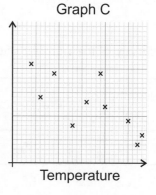

Temperature   Temperature   Temperature

a) Below are three labels for the vertical axes.
Write the letter of the appropriate graph next to each label.

sales of hot chocolate   ....

sales of ice-pops   ....

sales of crisps   ....

[2]

b) State the strength and type of correlation in graph C.

....

[1]

Score: ☐ out of **7**

Section 5 — Probability and Statistics

Key Stage 3
Mathematics Test

Practice Paper 1
Calculator NOT allowed

Maths

KEY STAGE
3

PRACTICE PAPER
1

Instructions

- The test is one hour long.

- Make sure you have these things with you before you start:
  pen, pencil, rubber, ruler, angle measurer or protractor
  and pair of compasses. You may use tracing paper.

- The easier questions are at the start of the test.

- Try to answer all of the questions.

- Don't use any rough paper — write all your answers and
  working in this test paper.

- Check your work carefully before the end of the test.

 This means write down
your answer or show your
working and your answer.

 You may not
use a calculator
in this test.

Formulas

Trapezium

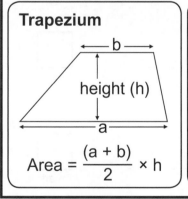

Area = $\frac{(a + b)}{2} \times h$

Prism

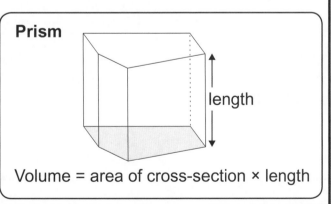

Volume = area of cross-section × length

Score: [   ] **out of 60**

CGP

1. Fill in the missing numbers in these calculations.

(a)  74 + ☐ = 82

1 mark

(b) ☐ × 5 = 45

1 mark

2. Shade two more squares so that the shape below has just one line of symmetry which is shown by the dashed line.

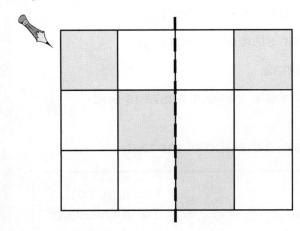

1 mark

3. Order the following sets of numbers from lowest to highest:

(a) 3459, 370, 3071, 469

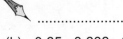 ....

1 mark

(b) 0.65, 0.603, 0.06, 0.136

....

1 mark

4. A tutor group consists of 7 boys and 3 girls.
The tutor chooses a pupil at random to run an errand.
Give the probability, as a fraction, that the teacher will pick:

(a) a boy

.... 1 mark

(b) a girl

.... 1 mark

5. A car park costs £1.95 to park for the first hour and £1.15 for each hour after that.
Alan wants to park for 2 hours.

(a) How much will it cost him?

£ .... 1 mark

(b) How much change will he get from a £5 note?

£ .... 1 mark

6. Give the names of the quadrilaterals from the descriptions.

(a) Four equal sides and four equal angles.

.... 1 mark

(b) Four equal sides and two pairs of equal angles.

.... 1 mark

(c) Two pairs of equal sides and two pairs of equal angles.

.... 1 mark

7. Katy takes part in a sponsored swim. The amount of money she raises depends on the number of lengths of the pool she manages to swim. This is shown on the graph below.

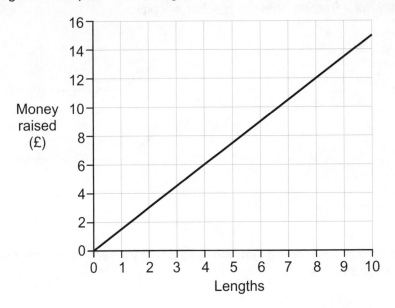

(a) Katy plans to swim 8 lengths of the pool. How much money would this raise?

 £ ....

1 mark

(b) Katy ended up raising £9. How many lengths of the pool did she swim?

 ....

1 mark

8. Fill in the next two numbers in each of the following sequences.

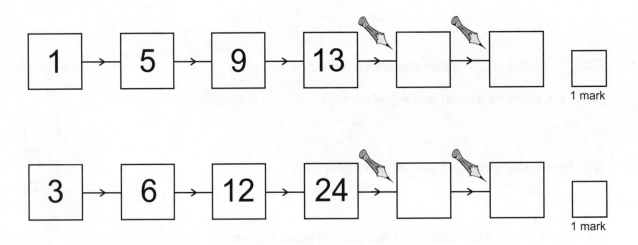

1 mark

1 mark

9. Laura, Sebastian and Chris are sharing a pie.

Laura eats 30% of the pie, Sebastian eats a quarter and Chris eats $\frac{2}{5}$.

(a) What fraction of the pie did Laura eat?
Give your fraction in its simplest form.

....

1 mark

(b) What percentage of the pie does Chris eat?

.... %

1 mark

(c) What percentage of the pie isn't eaten?

.... %

2 marks

10. In football, goal difference = total goals scored – total goals let in.

The table below shows the goal difference of five football teams, calculated from the results of all the games they've played so far this year.

Team	Goal Difference
A	-9
B	12
C	-4
D	7
E	-6

(a) Which teams have let in more goals than they've scored?

....

1 mark

(b) In the next game Team C won 5-0 against Team A.
Find the goal difference of each these teams after the game.

Team A: .... Team C: ....

2 marks

11. (a) Josh got the following marks out of 10 for his homework last month: **5**, **7**, **8**, **10**.
What was his median mark?

1 mark

(b) During the previous month he also handed in 4 pieces of homework.
They were all marked out of 10, and he got 10 once and 8 twice.
The range of his marks for that month was 5.
What was his other mark that month?

1 mark

(c) What was Josh's modal mark over the last two months?

1 mark

12. The triangle in the diagram is isosceles.

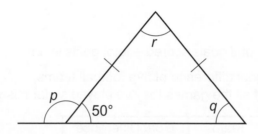

(a) Find the size of angle *p*.

p = ...°

1 mark

(b) Find the size of angle *q*.

q = ...°

1 mark

(c) Find the size of angle *r*.

r = ...°

1 mark

13. Look at the shape below.

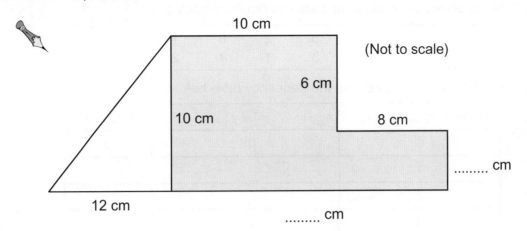

10 cm

(Not to scale)

6 cm

10 cm

8 cm

.... cm

12 cm

.... cm

(a) Fill in the two missing lengths marked on the diagram.

2 marks

(b) Find the area of the shaded part of the shape.

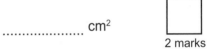

.... cm²

2 marks

(c) Find the total area of the shape.

.... cm²

2 marks

14. Simplify the following expressions.

(a) $a + a + a + a + a$

....

1 mark

(b) $3b \times 4b$

....

1 mark

(c) $3(2c - 5) + 2c$

....

2 marks

15. Penny kept track of the number of cups of tea she drank each day for 20 days.
The data below shows the number of cups she drank on each day.

3	0	4	2	3	2	0	1	3	1
0	2	2	2	3	1	4	2	4	1

(a) Use the data above to complete the frequency table below.

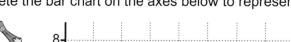

Number of cups of tea	Tally	Frequency
0	III	3
1		
2		
3		
4		

1 mark

(b) Complete the bar chart on the axes below to represent the data.

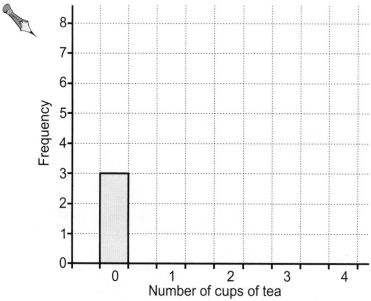

1 mark

(c) On what fraction of the last 20 days did Penny drink more than 2 cups of tea?

....

1 mark

16. Solve the equation $2x + 15 = 5x$.

$x =$ ....

2 marks

17. Paula makes a scale drawing of a room using the scale 1 : 100.

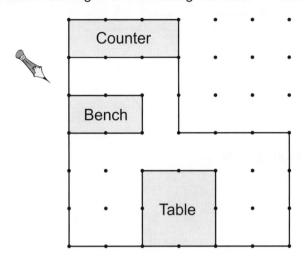

(a) What is the real-life side length of the table?

.... m

(b) Paula's new sofa is 3 m long and 1 m wide.

(i) What length and width should her sofa be on the scale drawing?

length = ... cm   width = ... cm

(ii) On the scale drawing above, draw the sofa in the room so that it is not touching any other piece of furniture.

18. Jordan cycled 100 miles in 8 hours.

(a) How many km did Jordan cycle?

.... km

(b) What was Jordan's average speed in km/h?

.... km/h

19. The medal below is in the shape of a regular polygon.

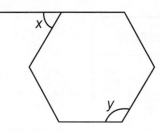

(a) Work out the size of the exterior angle *x*.

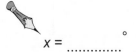

$x =$ ....°

1 mark

(b) Work out the angle of interior angle *y*.

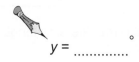

$y =$ ....°

1 mark

20. The recipe below shows the ingredients needed to make three pizza bases.

600 g plain flour
6 g of yeast
20 ml olive oil
300 ml water
60 ml milk

(a) Give the ratio of plain flour to yeast in its simplest form.

....

1 mark

(b) How much milk is needed to make nine pizza bases?

.... ml

2 marks

(c) If 1.2 litres of water is used to make a batch of pizza bases,
how many grams of plain flour are needed?

.... g

2 marks

(d) Lauren is making pizza bases but only has 24 g of yeast.
How many pizza bases she can make?

....

2 marks

Key Stage 3 Mathematics Test

Practice Paper 2
Calculator allowed

Instructions

■ The test is one hour long.

■ Make sure you have these things with you before you start:
pen, pencil, rubber, ruler, angle measurer or protractor,
pair of compasses, calculator. You may use tracing paper.

■ The easier questions are at the start of the test.

■ Try to answer all of the questions.

■ Don't use any rough paper — write all your answers and
working in this test paper.

■ Check your work carefully before the end of the test.

 This means write down
your answer or show your
working and your answer.

 You may use
a calculator
in this test.

Formulas

Trapezium

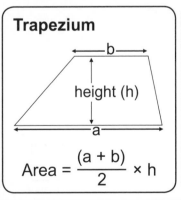

Area = $\dfrac{(a + b)}{2} \times h$

Prism

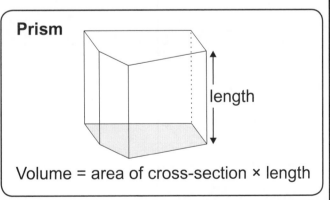

Volume = area of cross-section × length

Score: ☐ out of 60

1. (a) Write the number 2 150 703 in words.

....

....

1 mark

(b) The figure 7 in 2 150 703 has value 700.
What value does the figure 5 have? ....

1 mark

2. (a) What number should you subtract from 1000 to make 427?

....

1 mark

(b) What number should you multiply 25 by to make 1000?

....

1 mark

(c) How much bigger is half of 850 than one third of 960? Show your working.

....

2 marks

3. (a) On the axes below plot the points A = (-3, 2), B = (2, 2), C = (2, -1) and D = (-3, -1).
Join the points with 4 straight lines to make the shape ABCD.

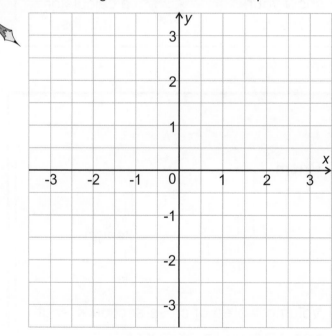

2 marks

(b) What is the name of shape ABCD? ....

1 mark

4. This pictogram below shows the number of miles Simon cycled on his four-day cycling holiday.

Friday	⊕ ⊕ ⊕
Saturday	⊕ ⊕ ⊕ ⊕
Sunday	⊕ ⊕ ◖
Monday	

Key
⊕ = 20 miles

(a) Simon cycled 40 miles on Monday.
Complete the pictogram above to represent this data.

1 mark

(b) How far did Simon cycle in total on his holiday?

.... miles

1 mark

5. One Saturday the attendance at a football match was 11 623.

(a) The local paper always gives the attendance to the nearest thousand.
Write down, in figures, the attendance to the nearest thousand.

....

1 mark

(b) The local radio station always gives the attendance to the nearest hundred.
Write down, in figures, the attendance to the nearest hundred.

....

1 mark

6. (a) Write down the first six multiples of 6.

....

1 mark

(b) Write down the first six multiples of 9.

....

1 mark

(c) What is the lowest common multiple of 6 and 9?

....

1 mark

7. The graph below shows the maximum and minimum temperatures over a week in the UK.

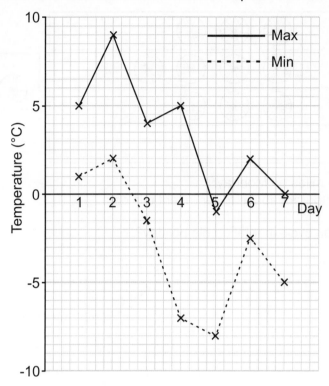

(a) What was the maximum temperature on day 3?

 ....°C

(b) What was the minimum temperature over the week?

 ....°C

(c) Which day had the largest temperature difference?

 ....

8. Eastwatch leisure centre charges the following prices for using the gym and pool:

| Gym: £4.50 | Pool: £2.20 | Gym and Pool: £5.50 |

In one afternoon 21 people only used the gym, 28 people only used the pool and 12 people used both. How much money did the leisure centre make that afternoon? Show your working.

£.............................

9. The timetable below shows some times for the ferry around Lake Conimere.

Winderton	10:20	10:50	11:20	11:50
Utherwaite	10:48	11:18	11:48	12:18
Grimtown	11:03	11:33	12:03	12:33
Roughton	11:33	12:03	12:33	13:03

(a) How many minutes are there between the start times of each ferry journey?

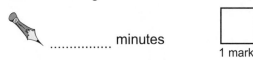 .... minutes

1 mark

(b) How long does it take for a boat to get from Winderton to Roughton?

 .... minutes

1 mark

(c) Christie lives in Utherwaite. She has lunch booked at a hotel in Grimtown at 12:15. The hotel is 5 minutes walk from where the ferry docks.

What time is the latest boat she can get from Utherwaite that will get her to Grimtown in time for her lunch?

....

1 mark

10. The diagram shows two cuboids with the **same volume**.

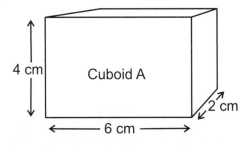
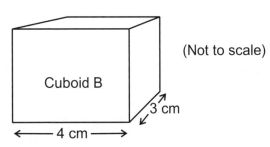

(Not to scale)

(a) What is the volume of Cuboid A?

 .... cm³

1 mark

(b) Find the height of cuboid B.

.... cm

2 marks

11. The triangle below is not drawn to scale.

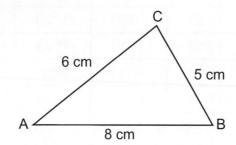

(a) Accurately construct this triangle in the space below.
Label the corners and sides of the triangle, as above.

3 marks

(b) Use a protractor to measure the angle ACB.

 ....°

1 mark

12. (a) Complete the factor tree below.

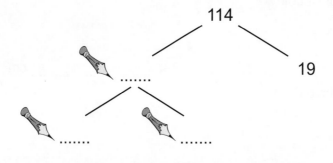

2 marks

(b) Express 114 as the product of prime factors.

....

1 mark

13. There are 240 pupils in Year 7 at Allerdale School.

> 80 of the pupils do French and Spanish.
> 50 of the pupils only do Spanish.
> 90 pupils don't do French or Spanish.

(a) How many pupils only do French?

....

1 mark

(b) Complete the Venn diagram below to show the number of pupils doing each language.

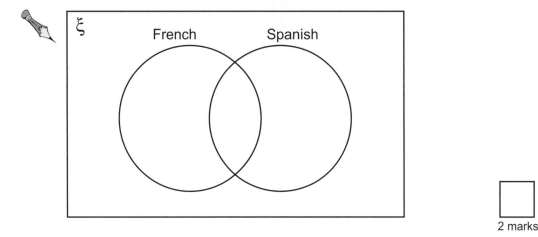

2 marks

14. The diagram below is not drawn to scale.

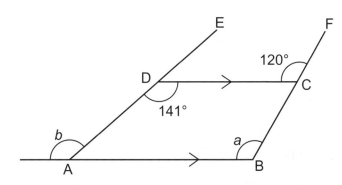

(a) What is the size of angle *a*? Give a reason for your answer.

....

....

2 marks

(b) What is the size of angle *b*? Give a reason for your answer.

....

....

2 marks

Practice Paper 2

15. (a) Complete the table of values for the equation $y = 2x - 1$.

x	0	2	4
y			

1 mark

(b) Use your table of values to draw the graph of $y = 2x - 1$ on the axes below.

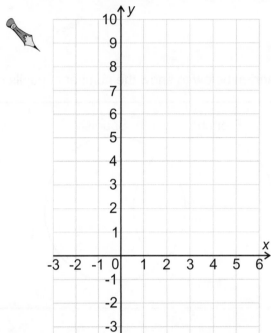

1 mark

(c) Use your graph to give the coordinates of the point where the line crosses the *x*-axis.

 ....

1 mark

16. A model railway track is in the shape of a circle with radius 1.5 m.

(a) What is the diameter of the model railway track?

 .... m

1 mark

(b) Calculate the circumference of the model railway track.
Give your answer to the nearest whole metre.

 .... m

1 mark

17. A hardware shop is changing the prices of its small and large toolboxes.

    (a) A small toolbox is increasing in price by 30%. The current price is £14.20.
        By how much (in pounds) will the price of a small toolbox increase?

£........................

1 mark

    (b) A large toolbox is decreasing in price by 20%. The current price is £38.10.
        What will the new price of a large toolbox be?

£........................

2 marks

18. In the diagram below, each box is the sum of the two preceding boxes.

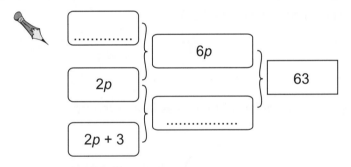

    (a) Fill in the empty boxes.

2 marks

    (b) Form an equation and find p. Show your working.

p = ...

3 marks

19. Shapes A and B have been drawn on the coordinate grid below.

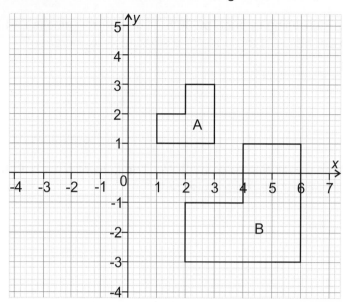

(a) Complete the sentence below to describe the enlargement that maps shape A onto shape B.

Shape B is an enlargement of shape A by scale factor ....

with centre of enlargement ....

2 marks

(b) Are shapes A and B similar, congruent or neither?

....

1 mark

20. The pie chart shows the proportions of different fruit trees in an orchard.

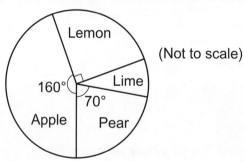

(Not to scale)

(a) What is the angle of the "Lime" sector of the pie chart?

.... °

1 mark

(b) There are 64 apple trees.
What is the total number of trees in the orchard?

....

2 marks